The Happiness Lab

Delegate's Guide

Paul Griffiths & Sharon Lanfear

UGLY
DUCKLING
PUBLISHING

Published by Ugly Duckling Publishing
Claremont House
Lydney
Gloucestershire
GL15 5DX
Email: office@theuglyducklingcompany.com
www.thehappinesslab.org

First edition 2016
Printed and bound in the UK

ISBN: 978-0-9935922-1-8

Acknowledgments
Miranda Lever (Editor) and Paul Worthy (Designer).

Happiness comes from living well. You live well when you realise you are a spiritual person in a material age.

Paul Griffiths and Martin Robinson

The Happiness Lab

The aim of The Happiness Lab is to create space to allow you to explore what psychologists, doctors, and faith leaders have to say about happiness. It gives you the opportunity to meet with people on a similar adventure and to learn from each other.

The experiment

The Happiness Lab is a six-session experiment that looks at the disciplines that develop a happier life. Topics explored include gratitude and savouring, kindness, forgiveness, friends and family, body and soul, and developing coping strategies.

Format

The shape of each session will depend on whether you are watching the fly-on-the-wall documentary series or engaging with an accredited facilitator. Ingredients will include input from experts, discussion, and refreshments.

How to get the best out of the course

Try and attend as many sessions as possible. Each week can be viewed independently but there is no doubt that the more sessions you attend, the more you will get out of the course.

Enjoy yourself

Our goal, and the objective of your course facilitators, is to create a meaningful and helpful space for you to explore the subject of happiness. Our hope is that you enjoy this course and find it beneficial. What is important is that you feel at home and take the opportunity to either sit back and listen or sit forward and engage fully in the conversation.

How to use the workbook

Each chapter contains several components that have been included to stimulate your thinking and experience as you engage with The Happiness Lab. Items include an introduction to each theme, questions to ponder, personal reflections from people who have attended the course previously, advice from experts, exercises to try which are connected to each session's discipline, a factoid, and an opportunity to begin journaling.

Journaling

It is a well-known thought that journaling helps with your thought processes. We have provided one or two pages in each session to get you started. However, if you find that this is not enough, or you carry on journaling after the course, then we have created a happiness journal which connects to the course, or you can perhaps buy a handy notebook for this purpose.

Try to read the *The 8 Secrets of Happiness* between sessions
To accompany the course there are a number of books that you can engage with. The Happiness Lab is inspired by *The 8 Secrets of Happiness*. Other books created by us to aid your experience of this resource include 101 Happiness Experiments, A Happiness Journal, and a mindfulness drawing book. All of these are available from The Happiness Lab website or your course leader.

Seek professional help if necessary

Sometimes we need to seek professional help if we are feeling particularly down, or if we feel that life is getting the better of us. The Happiness Lab does not attempt to replace you seeking medical help; in fact our hope is that this course will encourage you to go and see your doctor or other professionals if, in working through the material, you realise that life is not how it should be for you. There is nothing to fear in going to see your doctor; you should be proud of your action and make an appointment as soon as possible.

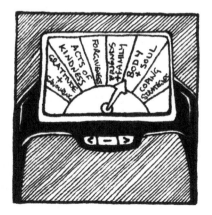

04

Friends & Family

05

Body & Soul

06

Coping Strategies

01
_
Gratitude &
Savouring

Seeing life differently

I n the film *The Colour of Paradise*, Iranian director and screenwriter Majid Majidi introduces us to Mohammad, a delightful and sensitive eight-year-old boy. Every summer, he excitedly leaves Tehran's Blind Institute in order to spend his holiday at home with his father and grandmother. Due to his inability to physically see, Mohammad has developed the capacity to look at life through the eyes of his heart. As someone who is filled with life, he is continually exploring that which is going on around him. Mohammad is treasured by his grandmother, but not by his father. During a summer that should have seen Mohammad flourishing in the countryside around

his home he is sadly taken away and placed as an apprentice to a blind carpenter. Mohammad's father, whose marriage is fast approaching, sees his son as an obstacle and is keen to offload him as quickly as possible. Despite being the father of a child who is caught up in the awe and wonder of that which surrounds him, Mohammad's father is a man who cannot see the treasure in front of his own eyes. There is incredible power in being thankful. What psychology teaches us is that opening your eyes to the many good things that surround you and then savouring them gives you the capacity to nourish your soul and develop your happiness muscles.

Phil's story

Stepping out of the ordinary

For me, one of the biggest learning moments of being on The Happiness Lab was to do with the challenge to slow down a little and appreciate what is going on around me. I feel that the last ten years have flown by, and although there have been some very good times in my life, I am not sure that I have enjoyed or savoured them as much as I could have. In being married with a family and being busy running a business it is easy to be caught up in what happens next rather than lingering a little longer in the good that is happening now. One of the experiences that brought this home to me happened when I was doing some chores at home. For a very brief moment in time, I managed to step out of the ordinary events of my day, turn the radio off and spend five minutes focussing on the washing-up. As I was drawn in to what I was doing, I could feel the soap and the heat of the water on the plates. That simple act of focussing in on what I was doing took me out of the busyness of the day and probably relaxed me for about five to seven minutes. After I had finished the washing-up, I dried my hands – by which time the phone was ringing and I was back in the hustle and bustle of the day. But that little bit of total downtime as I concentrated on the washing-up reorientated me to be more aware of what was going on right there and then, rather than being caught up in the many tasks that constantly call for my attention.

Happiness Experiments

I n his book *Affluenza*, Oliver James suggests that many people are infected by the disease of wanting to consume as much as possible. Those who suffer from this ailment often exhibit signs of profound emotional distress. What James goes on to observe is that those who have developed the capacity to be thankful and savour the good things that they have remain well. So, how do you develop these disciplines?

12

Keep a gratitude journal
The benefit of doing this is that it encourages a routine of reflection and acknowledgment of the good things that have happened recently, and acts as a memory bank for when good experiences are less frequent.

Write a gratitude letter
There is enormous joy received in dropping a line to someone and expressing your thanks for something good they have done – however little it may seem.

Make a gratitude visit
Identified as one of the most powerful happiness boosters, visit someone who has been good to you in some way and say thank you.

Say "thank you" more
These are two of the most powerful words that we can say to someone. Make it a habit of going through each day expressing your gratitude.

Thank-you meal
Plan a meal with those who have been kind to you.

Celebrate special days
There are certain days that we should celebrate. They are days to look forward to and prepare for; days that create good memories that we can dine on for weeks, if not years, to come.

Share the experience with others
There is enormous joy in reminiscing with others who have been involved in an adventure, or in simply sharing your first-hand experience of something with friends.

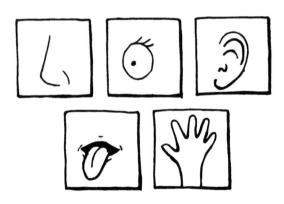

Engage all your senses in the moments of today.

Thank you

Arabic – shukran
[shoe-krahn]

Cantonese – do jeh
[daw-dyeh]

Czech – dêkuji
[deh-ku-yih]

Finnish – kiitos
[kee-tohss]

German – danke
[dahn-keh]

Hebrew – toda
[toh-dah]

Indonesian – terima kasih
[t'ree-ma kas-seh]

Italian – grazie
[grats-yeh]

Japanese – arigatou
[ahree-gah-tow]

Korean – kamsa hamnida
[kahm-sah ham-nee-da]

Mandarin – xièxie
[syeh-syeh]

Norwegian – takk
[tahk]

Portuguese – obrigado
[oh-bree-gah-doh]

Russian – spasibo
[spah-see-boh]

Sri Lankan – istutiy
[isst-too-tee]

Swahili – asante
[ah-sawn-tay]

SOMETHING TO PONDER

14

What can you be thankful for today? How do you spot the good things that happen in your life? **How do you become an ungrateful person?** How do you cultivate a more grateful heart? **Who should we be grateful to: only ourselves, the actions of others, or a divine power?** What does savouring mean to you? **What helps you savour an experience?** What is your top tip for slowing down to savour an experience? **What hinders you from savouring?** Why does personal loss or tragedy make some people more grateful? **How does savouring make you happier?** Most miserable person you know? **What piece of music do you find yourself lost in?** Describe a precious memory or the most precious gift you have ever been given. **Is savouring about the journey, the destination, or both? Why?**

Being fully present

Dr Martin Seligman, the father of positive psychology, notes that one of the three keys for raising your happiness level is getting more pleasure out of your life. The other two involve finding meaning and being more involved in what you do. Drawing greater pleasure from life includes savouring the experiences that you go through and learning to appreciate what you have. The three steps you can take to increase the pleasure that you have in life are:

Step 1: noticing the good things that you have or that are going on around you

Step 2: savouring those positive ingredients in your life

Step 3: being thankful for them.

When it comes to understanding what it means to savour, some of the following sentiments have been expressed:

It means getting as much good out of something – such as an experience or situation – as possible.

As humans we have a natural tendency towards negativity; this means that savouring is about treating a negative event as we would a positive one. Rather than mulling over what went wrong, why it went wrong, and dwelling on the negative emotions that we have, it is about realising how good that event was, why it was so good, and how positive we felt about it.

It is about being fully present in an experience.

We savour a situation when we bring all of our senses to that which we are savouring.

It is about not multi-tasking but focussing in on that one thing.

Some would say it's about giving your full attention to what is going on and absorbing the positivity.

Mindfulness is a word that is often equated with savouring; it means to be fully present and aware of what is going on around you *and* inside you.

We need to give ourselves permission, time, and space to be in the moment.

Rather than seeing life as a destination, it is better to perceive it as a journey, and to savour each step.

It requires slowing down and, on occasion, stopping.

A thankful heart

Add some thoughts of your own...

CULTIVATORS

- One thing at a time
- Slow down
- Focus
- Noticing/Paying Attention

KILLERS

- Multi-tasking
- Too busy

Journal

Don't forget to read this
week's chapter of *The 8
Secrets of Happiness*.

02

—

Kindness

The noble life

One of the most dramatic illustrations of someone living a kind life is that exhibited by ex-convict Jean Valjean in the novel *Les Misérables*. If kindness epitomises the qualities of being friendly, generous, and considerate, then Valjean lives this out in his dealing with Cossette, the daughter of one of his anonymous and insignificant factory workers. Valjean takes responsibility for Cossette in line with the deathbed request of her mother. With a plot set in 19th-century France, we see this one man shine out in the darkness of despair as again and again he expresses incredible acts of kindness to ensure Cossette's happiness. Whether people are kind for selfish reasons or altruistic ones, there is no doubt that there is incredible power in being kind to others. As Valjean's life illustrates, its impact can be felt physically, emotionally, and spiritually.

Lee's story

Thinking about others

After two years at university I felt that this route wasn't the best one for me and so decided to leave. I was doing fine academically, but with no clear career path ahead of me I decided to do something completely different. Now I work at a betting shop and am enjoying the responsibility of my new job as well as the social element. In attending The Happiness Lab one of the sessions that I found very useful was the one on practising acts of kindness. I wouldn't say that I wasn't a kind person, but I don't think that I was actively doing random acts of kindness for others. I didn't spend every day looking for someone I could do something good for. One of the principles that has helped me develop a kinder approach to life has been that of reflecting each evening on the day's opportunities to be kind that I have either taken up or missed. I then resolve to act better the following day. It has also helped me to move through the day looking out for new ways to be kind. My brother recently went off to university. With a mix of my own university experience, and having been thinking about acting kindly to others, I find myself regularly on the phone to him offering

21

him support with his work and with anything else that he could do with a helping hand for. I keep asking myself: What might he need help with? I never really thought through what the impact on me would be after doing kind things for others. It seemed the right thing to do. What I have discovered is that I have better relationships, I am kinder to myself having being kind to others, I am prouder of the person I am, and am more confident and sure of myself.

Happiness Experiments

There are many ways to express kindness and thereby cheering on the life of others. What follows below are some initial suggestions for expressing kindness; what is important is that you find what works for you and try and excel at it.

Smile

Sadly, in today's society you have to be careful about who you smile at, when you smile, and how big your smile is – but all that aside – smile!

Words

Words have power. Take time to speak kind, positive, life-giving words to those around you.

Listen

Many people today feel incredibly lonely. Schedule an opportunity to catch up with and listen to a family member or close friend.

Help

From time to time we all need a helping hand: someone who cuts the grass, or paints the fence, or does our shopping for us. There are occasions when opening the door for someone or offering a neighbour a lift can make their lives that little bit easier.

Wisdom

The pay off of growing older is learning some of the lessons that life teaches. What about offering some time to help at your local school or youth group and share your wisdom with others? You might be surprised by the fact that you may even learn one or two things yourself.

Surprise

Break in to the mundane life that many people live and surprise them with your presence, a gift (some baking, perhaps?), or good news.

Bake someone a cake.

The Good Eritrean

One night a businessman was driving down from Birmingham Airport to Cardiff. The flight from the conference had got in late and there were no trains at that time of night. He was tired and thought the back roads might keep him more alert. Up ahead of him on a long country road, probably built by the Romans, he spotted a breakdown and someone waving him in to the lay-by. For a moment he considered driving on, but thought better of it and pulled in. The bonnet on the other car was up and the driver beckoned him over: "It's knackered, mate, and I've no breakdown cover – you couldn't give me a lift to town could you?" The businessman was just about to say, "Of course," when he was struck from behind – back of the head, then kidneys, and a couple of kicks in the ribs as he went down. He heard a rib crack then felt it break a fraction of a second later. There turned out to be three of them; they rifled through his pockets, taking his wallet and phone, spotted his laptop and sales gear in the car and took them all. They then fled, laughing into the night, but not without first making sure the businessman was in no fit state to drive by administering further violent blows on him. Slowly, and in pain, the man propped himself up against his car hoping to flag down a passing motorist. A magistrate was driving home after a truly convivial Rotary Club dinner, saw the man up ahead, and remembered the kind of people he dealt with in court and what they could get up to. He accelerated past. It had been an eighteen-hour shift at the hospital for the doctor who next drove down the road. She was in no fit state to do anything but keep awake long enough to get home and to crawl in to bed. Compassion flared momentarily as she drew closer and saw what a state the businessman was in, but she simply couldn't face yet another patient. Reluctantly, and with a heavy, guilty heart, she drove past. An Eritrean asylum seeker, who by law shouldn't have been working at all, was doing night-delivery work, reckoning that it was probably the safest way to go undetected. It was terrible money of course, way below what they called the "national living wage" – but then he'd really work for anything when the alternative was sitting around all day going quietly mad. When he spotted the businessman in trouble he pulled over, helped him ever so carefully into his van, and drove to the nearest hospital, thinking it was quicker than calling an ambulance to such a remote spot at this time of night. When he got to the hospital he gave the businessman his mobile phone and his last £20 and promised to return the next night to see how he was. After all, he himself had been on the wrong end of violence like that back home – although that had been ordered by the government. Now which one of these three – the JP, the doctor, or the Eritrean – proved to be a neighbour and showed him kindness? And what does that mean for you and for me?

by Nigel Rooms

23

SOMETHING TO PONDER

24

Why are people kind? Why does seeing someone being kind or experiencing kindness have such an awe-inspiring impact? How does being kind make you happier? How can you become a kinder person? In what practical ways can we be kind to others? What stops people from being kind? Do you agree that we need an epidemic of kindness in the home? Why? What are your top tips for showing kindness in the home? Should you only be kind to people that you know? Why do some people find it difficult to accept the kindness of others? Who is the kindest person you know? Describe a time when someone demonstrated kindness to you. What does it mean to be kind? Who was the kindest person in history? Was the Good Eritrean a kind person or a stupid person?

What does a kind person look like?

Use words or pictures.

26

Happiness depends upon ourselves

Aristotle

Journal

Don't forget to read this
week's chapter of *The 8
Secrets of Happiness.*

03

—

Learning to Forgive

A better future

Does anyone deserve to be forgiven? The answer to that question, in all probability, is usually no. So why in The Happiness Lab do we spend a whole session encouraging delegates to consider offering the gift of forgiveness to those who have harmed them? The primary reason for encouraging individuals to forgive is that the act of forgiving someone is good for you. We do have a choice of whether to forgive someone or not. We also have every right never to reconcile with someone who has intentionally caused us pain. However, should you choose to make the difficult journey to forgive, which does not imply forgetting or pardoning or reconciliation, then there are several good reasons for doing so. Offering forgiveness enables us to break free from the cycle of bitterness and revenge; it improves our health; it opens up the possibility of restored relationships; and it works for the good of society. What offering forgiveness also does is to create a new ending to the story. Stories can have one of three endings: revenge, tragedy, or forgiveness. Forgiveness is the only option that can lead to freedom.

Penny's story

Not taking baggage with you

Some time ago, a close family member did something that hurt me and the rest of my family. It can be difficult to forgive someone when they have just hurt you, but when what they have done impacts on other people that you love, then the pain you feel seems to be far more intense. Their actions so upset me that I didn't seem to be able to let it go. I found myself going over it again and again. Not only did it tie me up in a knot, but even being in the same room as them was painful for me. As we all know, to forgive someone means different things to different people. For some people it is about being able to be in the same room with the perpetrator again; for others it is about moving on as if nothing has happened; and for others still it is about the impact of the wrongdoing on themselves. There is no doubt that forgiving someone can be difficult, but what I learnt was that holding on to all that bad feeling was doing me more harm than good, so I suddenly decided to let it go. It was like a great weight had been lifted: I stopped being consumed by it and was able to get on with life. Nothing had changed, other than my mental attitude to what had happened. I realised

31

that forgiveness in whatever form it means to you is definitely good for you. I expressed this once in a drawing; moving to a place of forgiveness is like no longer carrying the baggage of anger, rage, feeling a victim, bitterness, or feeling haunted to a place where you feel that you can let all that baggage go. It is about feeling free, light, or being released. Considering what I now know about forgiveness, and thinking back over this time in my life, I wish I had come to the decision to forgive sooner – I could have saved myself so much heartache.

Happiness Experiments

Choosing to offer forgiveness to someone or not is your decision. If you should determine to break free from the pain that someone has caused you, to re-write history, or to make a shift in your thinking then you need to develop your forgiveness muscles. Noted below are some ways that you could do that.

Read the stories of others who have forgiven

Read a bestselling book that details the story of someone journeying to offer forgiveness to someone who caused them harm. If there is no book that grabs your attention then see what films are currently showing at the cinema.

Write a letter of forgiveness

Take time to write a letter to the person who wronged you. Express your pain and the consequences of their actions. Then, express your forgiveness. There is no need to send the letter.

Appreciate being forgiven

No one is perfect, so in all probability there will be someone in your past that you have intentionally hurt. Imagine how they must have felt by your actions and the shock you caused by hurting them. Hopefully they would have decided to forgive you. If so, consider the journey they must have travelled on to the place of reconciliation.

Imagine forgiveness

Spend some time mulling over what it would be like to forgive the person who did you wrong. Explore your negative feelings, consider the pain they caused, try and understand why they acted as they did, and mull over what steps you need to take to offer forgiveness.

Seek forgiveness of others

Is there anyone that you need forgiveness from? If appropriate, consider taking the time to either write them a letter or go to see them; let them know what you did and ask for their forgiveness.

Talking to those who have expressed forgiveness

Spend some time with someone who has expressed forgiveness to a person who has hurt them. Listen to them as they express their pain and journey to offering forgiveness.

Watch an inspiring film about forgiveness.

Steps to forgiveness

Weigh up if you want to forgive this person or not
No one can force you to forgive someone else. To make that choice you need to weigh up the pros and cons of doing so.

Personally journey to a place of forgiveness
As you journey to the place of forgiveness you must pass through the phases of recalling the hurt that you experienced, trying to understand why the person acted as they did, contemplation of moments when you have hurt others, and, finally, establishing a mindset where you desire to think differently about the person who hurt you.

Decide on the best way of expressing forgiveness – for you and them
You could go and see them with a friend and chat about what they did to you; you could write them a letter; you could decide to forgive them, but choose never to tell them that or see them again. Only you can decide what is the best way of expressing the forgiveness you have decided to grant.

Walk out your new mindset
This could mean anything from a restored relationship, to not talking negatively about someone to wishing them the best in life – yet having nothing to do with them yourself.

Hold on to forgiveness
After you have forgiven someone there will still be moments when you feel the pain of their hurt. At that moment you have to again acknowledge the journey you have gone on and remind yourself of your decision to forgive them.

Revenge

Definition
The act of causing injury or pain to someone who
has hurt you.

A moment of pleasure
When you first enact revenge on someone who has
harmed you, there is a feeling of justice.

Long-term effects
If you keep on thinking about getting revenge,
that causes a negative effect as it prolongs the
unpleasantness of the hurtful action.

Healthy way of dealing with revenge
Take the feelings and direct them towards
achieving something good in life.

"The best revenge is massive success."
Frank Sinatra

Create or find...

...a symbol, poem, story or a piece of art or music that expresses what forgiveness means to you.

SOMETHING TO PONDER

What is your definition of forgiveness? What words do you associate with the word forgiveness? Should you forgive someone again and again? What should never be forgiven? Have you ever got revenge on someone who has hurt you? Is there someone you have never forgiven? What do you do when someone won't forgive you? Why is it difficult to forgive? What are some of the steps to forgiving someone? How can you develop your forgiveness muscles? Why do spiritual people find it easier to forgive people than those who are not spiritual? Is forgiveness a good thing? What is the most inspiring story you know about forgiveness? Do you need to be forgiven? What is the relationship between justice, mercy, and forgiveness?

Add some thoughts of your own…

pardoning

forgetting

excusing

37

Forgiveness is not…

condoning

implying denial of harm

reconciliation

Journal

Journal

Don't forget to read this week's chapter of *The 8 Secrets of Happiness*.

04
—
*Invest in
Friends & Family*

Two is better than one

42

Friends are good for you. The happiest people in the world are normally those with lots of good friends. It was once said that "two are better than one" and all the evidence supports the fact that a life lived in community with others is a happier life than one lived in isolation. Research conducted on three different continents among communities with elderly members revealed that, more than anything else, what these people had in common was that they were socially engaged: they had friends. Old age was not about keeping themselves to themselves but rather about getting out and connecting with others. There are many reasons why belonging is good for you: we can receive the support we require during life's difficult times; we have someone to share joyful experiences with which will deepen those experiences for us; other people are a mechanism for expressing and receiving love; and other people can create a safe place in which we can explore who we are and what we bring to the world. The challenge in all this is how do we make the right choices and manage our time accordingly so as to fully invest in the relationships we have with friends and family.

Adam's story

Spending time with friends and family

R elationships are challenging for me. Some time ago my wife left me. I didn't expect it to happen, nor was I looking for it to happen, but one of the consequences of it was that I focussed more on my work than I would have if things had been different. What is more, the nature of my job is such that as a web developer I spend a lot of time on my own. The primary means of communication with my clients is via email, so I don't really spend much time in face-to-face meetings. I was probably spending about eighteen hours a day at work with me sitting on my own at the computer 99 per cent of the time. Some people might have thought that I was a bit of a hermit. That said, I did focus on spending any free time I had with my kids. It frightened me how fast they were growing up and how quick things were changing. We all know that relationships are essential to happiness, but it is difficult when life doesn't go as you hoped it would and you have a job that doesn't give you as much free time as you would like. In being on The Happiness Lab I

realised how busy I was and that I had a cynical outlook on friendships. Since then I have tried to take a greater interest in, and think more about, other people. I have also made an extra effort to spend more time with friends and family and to put more into those relationships. This has made work more enjoyable and has made me a happier person too.

Happiness Experiments

When it comes to creating your own formula for happiness nearly everyone includes the importance of friends and family. So, with that being the case, it is important to take time to invest in these precious relationships. What follows below are several suggestions for how you can build more meaningful connections.

Cheer others on.

44

Cheer each other on
Achievements become sweeter when they are shared with others. When something good happens to a friend, or when they accomplish something (big or small), make a big deal out of it. If someone close to you is rising to a challenge, cheer them on; if they are finding the going quite tough then shout for them as loud as you can.

Make time
Relationships blossom when they are watered with time. Often, making time to invest in friendships is about choices in how you spend your time. Research indicates that choosing to spend time with friends raises our levels of happiness.

Appreciate
Everybody is a masterpiece being prepared for the big reveal. Take time to appreciate that which is good about those close to you.

Hug
There are some for whom a hug is awkward – in some circumstances even inappropriate – but where it is possible and welcome, take time to hug your friends – when you get together and when you say goodbye.

Forgive
Everyone gets it wrong at some point. There are moments when the best and most noble thing to do is to forgive and move on. This isn't saying that we should always forgive. If someone hurts you, forgiving them does not mean that you just let them hurt you again.

Reminisce
One of the great joys of life is being able to walk down memory lane with some close friends and tell the story again. Plan time with some of your oldest friends to do just that.

Destructive chat

Accusation
Harmful conversations begin with a harsh exchange of accusation and sarcasm: it's all your fault!

Criticism
Quite quickly the character of the other person involved is attacked. This often feels like war.

Defensive stance
Then comes: "It's not my fault, it's you; you're the one to blame."

Contempt
Those involved in the conversation feel contempt for each other. It isn't long before people are rolling their eyes at each other and having a look of disgust about them.

Stonewalling
Not listening to what the other person is saying or just walking out of the room while they are talking.

45

Active listening is...

more than simply listening to the words of the person speaking

hearing the deeper meaning contained in the words being spoken

focussing on the whole person speaking

not waiting for the other person to breathe so that you can jump in with what you have to say

sharing in the suspense of what is being said

causing the person speaking to leave feeling as if they have been heard.

SOMETHING TO PONDER

Is self-reliance good for you? Why are relationships good for you? What are the ingredients of healthy and unhealthy relationships? What are some of your top tips for deepening an existing relationship? Is conflict in a relationship always a bad thing? How do you manage conflict with your friends? Describe a special moment in one of your relationships. What advice would you give to someone who wanted to make new friends? Why are so many people lonely today? Which of your relationships are affected first when life gets busy? How good are you at saying "no" to the wishes and demands on your time that others make? Identify your key relationships. How important is it to be known by another person? Why do so many keep a pet? Describe a good listener.

Language of love

Marriage and family life expert Gary Chapman has identified that there are five languages of love. These are words, actions, time, gifts, and touch.

What is your language of love?

Thinking about the various relationships that you have, who has what love language and what is a way of illustrating it?

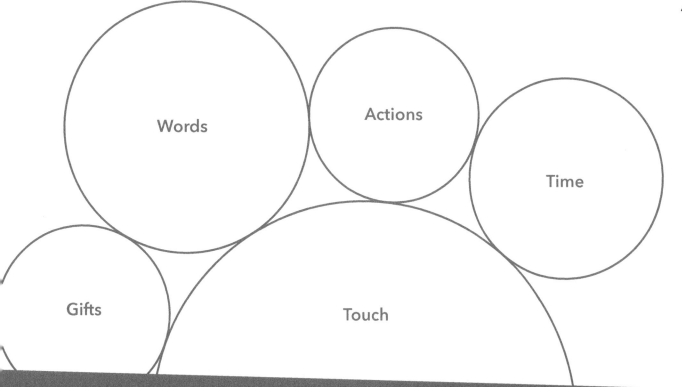

The most productive*
workers have a best
friend at work.

48

*up to 700% more engaged

http://www.cooleaf.com/blog/11-shocking-employee-happiness-statistics-that-will-blow-your-mind-infographic

Journal

Don't forget to read this
week's chapter of *The 8
Secrets of Happiness*.

05

—

*Look After Your
Body & Soul*

Holistic care

When it comes to caring for yourself, most people acknowledge that we need to look after our mind, body, and soul. Although there is some ambiguity as to what we mean by the terms "soul" or "spiritual", there is a general acceptance that they refer to an inner aspect of our being that gives definition to who we are. Ideas about how to look after your body, and indeed mind, are well documented: watch what you eat and drink; work on getting a good night's sleep; do an appropriate amount of exercise; and do puzzles and games that get your mind working. But how do we look after our soul? Admittedly, as whole beings, to look after our mind and body is to look after our soul. If we are in good shape physically we will feel better about who we are. When it comes to looking after your soul the key is to explore the wisdom of the ages and the practices of cultures from across the world today. Some will work and some will not. The best way forward is to dabble with a few at a time and see what works for you. Perhaps an ideal place to start is in the areas of laughter, celebration, and hospitality.

Alison's story

Getting off the treadmill

Before I started on this course, I thought that The Happiness Lab was just for unhappy and depressed people. As a professional businesswoman who leads a busy life running several businesses with my husband, caring for my family, and being involved in the community, I didn't think that it was going to be able to teach me anything. But having done the course, I am in total shock. The experience of spending six weeks working through the disciplines of a happy life taught me to pause and reflect, and gave me a greater ability to appreciate things more. It seems so obvious now, but there is very real power in slowing down and stopping. I had thought that I knew how to appreciate the little things in life, but after six weeks I had a new appreciation for the birds singing and my children playing and laughing. I think, like many people, I was on a treadmill running as fast as I could wanting to be happy. I lived life to the full; I was happy biting off more than I could chew, taking risks, pushing boundaries. I genuinely thought I knew who I was, what I thought, and was confident that I was a happy person. I believed that the faster I ran on that treadmill the happier I would be. But actually, what I learnt through being on this course was to stop running – that was scary and made me feel very vulnerable. This process also made me very cross because someone was showing me that I wasn't as happy as I thought I was. Now, I think I have a new depth to how I live my life: far more than the shallowness of just running on the treadmill as fast as you can.

Happiness Experiments

Plan a quiet day.

Whereas most magazines offer us advice about caring for ourselves physically and emotionally (food, friends, sleep, exercise, sex, balanced lifestyle) there is some uncertainty about how we express and nurture our spiritual intelligence. For that reason, what follows on the menu below are some pointers to develop your spiritual muscles. There is no need to try them all; pick a couple and give them a go.

Find a soul friend
Walking through life in the company of a friend makes sacred the path you travel. If you have someone in your life like this then take time to reconnect; if not, then consider how you could go about finding and nurturing such a friendship.

Celebration
Some people think that Jesus was often partying. Take time to celebrate life and the success of others.

Sacred place
It is good to have a place you can go to to find peace and quiet. A sacred place where it is easier to realise that you are not alone on this planet, that there is a hand that guides your life, and that there is hope for tomorrow. Take a few moments this week to visit that place.

Laughter
It is good to laugh. Watch a funny programme on TV, visit a comedy club, go and see a comedian, or read a book of jokes.

Hospitality
We meet something of the spiritual in the lives of others. Sharing a meal with friends or acquaintances will allow you to explore each other's stories.

Service
Often in the expressing of kindness to others we encounter something of the divine. Look for opportunities where you can help someone else.

Filtering voices
From when we wake up to the moment that we go to sleep there are people communicating to us. Whether it's the DJ on the radio, the lyricist of the song you are humming, or the commercials on TV, everyone has a message. Caring for your soul is about operating a filter that ensures that you only allow in that which *you* decide.

A good night's sleep

The National Sleep Foundation offers the following ten tips for a good night's sleep:

1. Maintain a regular bedtime and waketime schedule, including at weekends.

2. Establish a relaxing bedtime routine, such as soaking in a hot bath and then reading a book or listening to soothing music.

3. Create a sleep-conducive environment that is dark, quiet, comfortable, and cool.

4. Sleep on a comfortable mattress and pillow.

5. Use your bedroom only for sleep and sex. It is best to take work materials, computers, and TVs out of the sleeping environment.

6. Finish eating at least two or three hours before your regular bedtime.

7. Exercise regularly. It is ideal to complete your workout at least a few hours before bedtime.

8. Avoid alcohol, nicotine, and caffeine close to bedtime. These can contribute to poor sleep, keep you awake, or disrupt sleep later in the night.

9. We all know the importance of eating well. Ensure that you regularly get your quota of fruit and veg. It is also crucial to drink as much water as you need.

10. Work with your partner to have good and satisfying sex.

55

SOMETHING TO PONDER

Do you make time to look after yourself? What do you understand by the terms "body" and "soul"? How do you identify the positive and negative voices in your life? What positive choices are you making to ensure that you look after yourself physically? What advice would you give to someone who wanted to develop their spiritual life? How do you know when your life is out of balance, and how do you rectify this? Are there certain ways that you can switch off and relax? What is your top tip for a good night's sleep? Do you have any rituals that keep you well? How do you manage your digital life? Is there a place you go to to find peace and quiet? If laughter is the best medicine, how do we laugh more? Do you pray? What one thing could you stop or start to look after yourself better? Why do you think looking after your body and soul will make you happier?

Happiest ways to commute

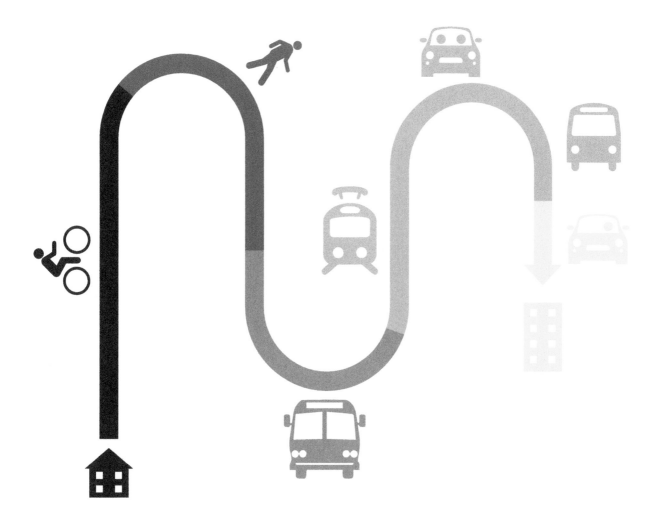

	Cycling	Walking	Express bus	Light rail	Carpool	Local bus	Driving alone
Well-being:	80%	72%	57%	43%	43%	35%	30%

http://bikeportland.org/2013/01/30/bike-commuters-are-happiest-and-other-psu-research-tidbits-82448

People who speak negatively into your life…

People who speak positively into your life…

Journal

Journal

Don't forget to read this
week's chapter of *The 8
Secrets of Happiness*.

06
_

Developing
Coping Strategies

When life doesn't go to plan

64

As M. Scott Peck noted in his book *The Road Less Travelled*, life is difficult. At some point or another almost everyone goes through suffering, pain, or damaging circumstances that they would rather avoid. For some people, life can seem like one continuous assault course. But how do you cope when life does not go as you hope or plan for? The purpose of The Happiness Lab is to explore ways of becoming a happier person. To achieve that goal we have to find strategies for managing the times when life is tough. It might be too optimistic to think that we can go through difficult times "singing and dancing" but could there be a way of accepting and enduring what is going on that will not only bring us through, but also help us grow; perhaps even give us a couple of good days? There is no one-size-fits-all when it comes to using coping strategies to deal with the sad times that life can create. What is important is to figure out what works for you – and excel at it. As a place to start, it could be useful to ask yourself the question "What if I… ?" The reason being that the more prepared you are in advance of entering a difficult time, the greater your resources.

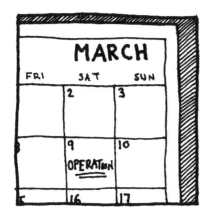

Mandy's story

A bit at a time

We all know that life can be tough. When life is difficult, sometimes I find it relatively easy to work through the situation. I feel that I have enough resilience to get through it. It's not a matter of plain sailing but I'm not as overwhelmed as I or others thought I would be. At other times, I find that I can get through whatever is happening by making sure that I employ some of the better-known coping mechanisms that we all use. It is great to have friends to call on or to be able to get away from it all for a few days. However, I have experienced a time when even these didn't produce the level of strength that I needed and so I found myself immobilised by what was going on. During that moment when nothing seemed to help me cope, I found that the best thing I could do was to be real about how I was going to manage the next few months or weeks. At the start, I didn't even know how I was going to get through the next week. Rather than feeling overwhelmed at the idea of getting through the next seven days, I broke that period of time down and set myself the challenge of getting through one day at a time. When it was too much to even think about getting through the next 24 hours, again, rather than feeling overwhelmed, I broke that down even further and thought about getting through the next hour. For me, this simple task of breaking down this time of difficulty into smaller chunks enabled me to move forward, one manageable step at a time.

Happiness Experiments

Life sucks. Not all the time, but there are moments in everyone's life when days become difficult. Whether the trouble we find ourselves in is a result of our own actions or those of another, or simply because that's the way life is, what is important is that we develop mechanisms for dealing with our lot in life.

Learn to say no

Store up positive thoughts
As you go through life store up for yourself positive experiences and thoughts so that when life is difficult you can draw on the positivity you have banked.

Call on friends
When life is tough there is sometimes nothing better than a shoulder to cry on or someone with whom you can talk through your issues. If life is difficult right now, why not schedule some time with a close friend.

Take time out
Being able to get away from what is going on in your life is a great coping mechanism. It might not be possible to take a two-week holiday, but even a ten-minute walk can help re-calibrate you.

Get yourself ready
If you know in advance that life is going to get a little difficult, think through what you can do to move through that period as well as possible.

Pray
People who pray often deal with difficulty easier than those who don't. It is helpful because you don't feel alone as you go through whatever it is that is troubling you, and it enables you to step outside your immediate situation.

A choice of two paths

Like every good movie there are four possible outcomes when life casts you in a difficult place. You can be crushed by it, survive it, recover from it, or thrive in it (though note we should not equate thriving with being hilariously happy). Writing the final scene is determined by how you deal with the situation you find yourself in. There are fundamentally two possible responses when you are struck by a personal crisis. Some people attempt to deal with their upsetting scenario by engaging in a problem-solving approach, while others attempt to adopt a more accepting response.

The problem-solving approach
For those who believe it is a matter of problem-solving, their approach is to obtain as much information as possible about the issues and then form a plan of action to deal with them. Often the biggest weakness of this route is that it deals with the effects and not the cause of what is going on.

Ingredients in this process include:

call the problem by its name

clarify what would take the problem away

consider all options for dealing with this issue

choose a particular route for solving your issues

calculate what could happen

carry out your plan

contemplate what happened.

The emotion-focussed approach
When it comes to approaching the difficult issues in a more accepting way, then we are thinking in terms of how to reduce the symptoms of stress of the particular context we are in. Not every situation we find ourselves in can be solved. When we are in that place we need to think in terms of how best to manage ourselves through the rollercoaster that we are about to get on. There are many emotion-focussed approaches that people use. These include *behavioural strategies* (different ways of acting while you are in this tough scenario) and *cognitive strategies* (thinking differently about your context).

As far as possible, practical things that you could do to engage in either of these responses would include going on holiday, engaging in a local project that helps others, or talking with friends.

SOMETHING TO PONDER

How easy do you find it to get back up after you have been knocked down? What are some of your coping mechanisms for when life is tough? How have your friends helped you during some of life's difficulties? Who can you turn to for help and advice when life gets tough? How easy is it to accept and endure the tough stuff that happens to you? Is it possible to be happy during tough times? Why does the world seem to be a broken place? Do you see problems as a setback, a challenge, or an opportunity? Is it important how you think about why life is tough? Where do you go in your self to find strength? Why do people pray during tough times? What are some of the ways that we can help others when they are going through a tough time? Who is the bravest person you know? What coping strategies do you have that are unhealthy? What is the worst thing that has ever happened to you, and how did you deal with it?

Add some thoughts of your own…

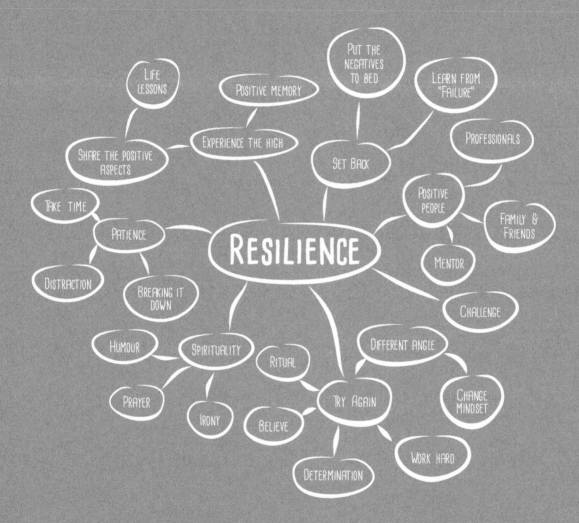

Journal

Don't forget to read this
week's chapter of *The 8
Secrets of Happiness*.

What's next?

We hope the you have enjoyed The Happiness Lab and that it has been useful to you as you have explored this theme. You might find that rather than everything now being neatly sewn up, you have even more questions, and that the questions you started with have become more profound.

All of this is quite normal.

For those of you who want to carry on exploring what it means to be a spiritual person in a material world, here are some suggestions for ways forward:

Keep in contact with those you have met on The Happiness Lab – both the leaders and other participants.

What about playing Table Talk together, a game of conversations: www.table-talk.org

Follow us on Facebook /theuglyducklingcompany and Twitter @uglyducklingco

One of the other resources that we have created is Puzzling Questions. Having identified some of the most popular questions asked by those interested in spirituality, this course aims to create safe and appropriate space for people to explore these questions. More information can be found at: www.theuglyducklingcompany.com

Sign up for Happy Hints. Do visit The Happiness Lab website regularly and take a look at the growing number of articles, features, and downloads available.

Consider doing The Happiness Lab again, but this time bring one of your friends with you.

Thank you for taking the time to attend The Happiness Lab. We do hope that it has been beneficial to you and that as you continue your journey it might contribute positively to what happens next.

Feedback

We want to know what you think about
The Happiness Lab: what worked, what didn't, and
how we could improve it. Go to The Happiness Lab
website and click on the link to our "What people
say" survey.

Website

There are additional videos and articles to engage
with as you explore the topic of happiness
www.thehappinesslab.org

Happy Hints

To sign up for our regular Happy Hints email,
please go to The Happiness Lab website and follow
the link.

Contribute

If you have any stories or items that you think could
be included in the Happy Hints newsletter, please
email them to office@thehappinesslab.org

Additional resources

The 8 Secrets of Happiness

Published by Lion Hudson and written by Paul Griffiths and Martin Robinson, this book explores what psychologists suggest are the keys to a happier life. In eight chapters this book unpacks the core content of The Happiness Lab.

101 Happiness Experiments

Written by Paul Griffiths, this book is not a one-size-fits-all programme to make you a happier person, but rather sets out 101 ideas for you to experiment with to help you find what makes you happier. Ideal companion for those on The Happiness Lab.

Lightning Source UK Ltd.
Milton Keynes UK
UKOW07f1643210217
294936UK00002B/14/P